Core Knowledge Language Arts®

Unit 3
Workbook

Skills Strand
GRADE 2

Amplify learning.

Core Knowledge®

ISBN 978-1-61700-221-2

Printed in the USA
09 LSCOW 2021

Unit 3
Workbook

This Workbook contains worksheets that accompany many of the lessons from the Teacher Guide for Unit 3. Some of the worksheets in this book do not include written instructions for the student because the instructions would have contained nondecodable words. The expectation is that teachers will explain these worksheets to the students orally, using the guidelines in the Teacher Guide. The Workbook is a student component, which means that each student should have a Workbook.

Dear Family Member,

The spelling words for this week include "r-controlled vowels." By itself, the letter 'r' is a spelling for a consonant sound, but the sound /r/ can mingle with certain vowel sounds, creating unique vowel sounds like /er/, /ar/, and /or/. Please remember to practice the spelling words for a short time (five to ten minutes) each night.

Today your child is also bringing home a story to read, "A Letter from the Publisher," and an accompanying worksheet. This is the first story in our Unit 3 Reader, *Kids Excel*. Your child will read about kids excelling at all types of things, such as spelling, jumping rope, and playing soccer. After reading "A Letter from the Publisher," have your child answer the story questions on the back of the worksheet. Encourage your child to look back at the story to find the answers.

'er'	'or'	'ar'
sister	born	mark
letter	sports	started
expert	short	backyard

Tricky Word: some

A Letter from the Publisher

Kids,

My name is Mark Deeds, and I have a fun job. I visit with kids who *excel* at what they do.

When you *excel* at something, you are good at it.

The kids I visit all excel at different things. Some of them excel at sports like running or jumping rope. Some of them excel at math. Some of them excel at skipping rocks or standing on their hands. All of them are good at something.

I visit with the kids. I chat with them. I ask them how they got started doing what they do and how they got good at it. Sometimes I chat with their moms and dads, too. I jot down notes and take snapshots. Then I write up what they tell me so I can share it with you.

In *Kids Excel* you will meet a lot of kids who excel. I had fun meeting them. I think you will like meeting them, too.

When I meet someone who excels at something, it inspires me to be as good as I can be. I hope the kids in *Kids Excel* have the same effect on you, too!

Mark Deeds

Publisher
Kids Excel

A Letter from the Publisher

1. If you *excel* at something, you are

   _____.

   A. good at it

   B. bad at it

   C. sick of it

2. Mark Deeds _____.

   A. hates his job

   B. has the best job

   C. is sick of his job

3. Mark Deeds _____.

   A. is a teacher

   B. is an artist

   C. is a publisher

4. Who writes the words that are printed in *Kids Excel*?

   A. Kids write the words.

   B. Mark Deeds hires men to write the words.

   C. Mark Deeds writes the words.

5. Use the box to draw yourself excelling at something.

[ ]

_____

_____

_____

_____

_____

_____

Name _____

Spelling Sort

Directions: Sort the words by their spellings. Write the words with the /ae/ sound spelled 'ai' under *rain*, the words with the /ae/ sound spelled 'ay' under *day*, and the words with the /ae/ sound spelled 'a_e' under *cake*. Then circle the /ae/ spellings in each word.

stain	paid	playing	raining	plate	hay
train	strayed	brains	say	rake	daytime
clay	bait	tray	make	pain	mistake

/ae/ spelled 'ai' as in *rain*

/ae/ spelled 'ay' as in *day*

/ae/ spelled 'a_e' as in *cake*

stain

The Spelling Bee

1. What do kids do in a spelling bee?

   _____

   _____

   _____

   _____

   Page _____

2. What sound do kids hear when they spell a word wrong?

   A. They hear the sound *boom*.

   B. They hear the sound *buzz*.

   C. They hear the sound *ding*.

   Page _____

3. How old are the spellers in the bee?

   _____

   _____

   _____

   _____

   Page _____

4. Who was the runner-up in the bee the year before?

_____

_____

_____

Page _____

5. Who do you think will be the winner of the spelling bee?

_____

_____

_____

Page _____

6. Write 5 words with the /ae/ sound and 5 words with the /a/ sound that could be used in a spelling bee.

/ae/	/a/
_____	_____
_____	_____
_____	_____
_____	_____

Name _____

Are the Sounds the Same?

Family Member Directions: Have your child read the pair of words. He or she should write yes if the underlined letters stand for the same sound, and no if they do not.

Word 1	Word 2	Are the sounds the same? Yes or No
r<u>ake</u>	r<u>ai</u>n	Yes
m<u>ai</u>n	w<u>ay</u>side	
<u>wr</u>ist	<u>w</u>et	
s<u>ay</u>	s<u>ai</u>d	
<u>kn</u>ock	<u>n</u>ot	
br<u>ake</u>	st<u>ai</u>n	
t<u>ai</u>l	t<u>a</u>l<u>e</u>	
cl<u>ay</u>	cl<u>a</u>m	
s<u>ai</u>lor	tr<u>ay</u>	
b<u>ea</u>n	b<u>e</u>nd	

Spelling Sort

Sort the words by spelling. Write the words with the /a/ sound spelled 'a' under *cat*, the words with the /ae/ sound spelled 'a' under *paper*, the words with the /ae/ sound spelled 'a_e' under *cake*, the words with the /ae/ sound spelled 'ai' under *paid*, and the words with the /ae/ sound spelled 'ay' under *tray*. Then circle the /ae/ or /a/ spelling in each word.

cat	paper	cake	paid	tray
shame	agent	race	acorn	cap
day	play	strain	radar	late
crane	faint	pain	snake	pray
napkin	basic	frame	tablet	David

'a'	'a'	'a_e'	'ai'	'ay'
cat	paper	cake	paid	tray

_____ _____ _____ _____ _____

_____ _____ _____ _____ _____

_____ _____ _____ _____ _____

_____ _____ _____ _____ _____

_____ _____ _____ _____ _____

And Then There Were Two

Directions: Have students answer the questions in complete sentences.

1. Which kid misspelled the word *penicillin*?

   _____

   _____

   Page _____

2. Which kid spelled the word *penicillin* without making a mistake?

   _____

   _____

   Page _____

3. What did Gail Day win?

   _____

   _____

4. What place was Gail Day in the spelling bee? What place was Nate Griffin?

   _____

   _____

   Pages _____

The Spelling Bee

This past spring I went to see the state spelling bee.

The state spelling bee is a spelling contest that lasts two days. On Day 1, a bunch of kids sit down to take a written spelling test. On Day 2, the kids who do the best on the written test get up on a stage and spell.

One hundred ten kids took the spelling test last spring. The kids had to spell words like *chimpanzee*. The 50 who did the best on the written test went on to Day 2 of the spelling bee.

Day 2 is the part of the bee I like best. That's when the kids get up on stage and spell words out loud.

A man will say a word. Then the speller has to spell the word one letter at a time. If the speller spells the word without a mistake, he or she gets to keep spelling. If the speller makes a mistake, a bell rings.

Ding!

Once the bell rings, that is the end. The speller is out of the bee. He or she

Directions: Have your child read the story with a family member and discuss the story afterwards.

must sit down in a chair and look on while the rest of the spellers stay in the bee and keep spelling.

On Day 2 of the bee I sat and looked on as the bell rang for lots of kids in the bee.

Airplane. A-e-r-p-l-a-n-e? *Ding!*

Graying. G-r-a-i-n-g? *Ding!*

Sunday. S-u-n-n-d-a-y? *Ding!*

The bell went on ringing all day, until there were just three spellers left.

Nate Griffin, age 12, was one of the three. He was the runner-up at the last spelling bee. Two of the experts I spoke with said they expected him to win the bee.

Craig Ping, age 12, was still in the hunt, too. He had finished in fifth place at the last bee. The experts I spoke with said he had a good chance of winning.

Gail Day, age 11, was the dark horse. When I asked the spelling experts who she was, they just shrugged.

Craig Ping was spelling well. Then he got a hard word. He stood thinking. He spelled the word as well as he could. He waited.

Ding!

Craig Ping was out of the bee. That left just Gail Day and Nate Griffin.

Fill in the Blanks

salad	habit	acorns	April	bacon
radish	baker	camel	later	label

1. There were many _____ on the ground next to the tree.

2. I will do that job at a _____ time.

3. I asked the waitress to put a _____ in my _____ for lunch.

4. Did you ever ride a _____?

5. _____ showers bring May flowers.

6. Biting your nails is a bad _____.

7. The _____ made a cake for us.

8. I like to eat _____ and eggs in the morning.

9. Please write your name in the space on the _____.

Directions: Have students choose the best word to complete the sentence.

the Milk

ther wuz a las namd jane

she tuk a bukt of milk to cell

jane fell don

she wuntd to by a dres she wantd to get
a pigg

jane wuz sad

the nd

To: Karen	not-so-good spelling	The Milk
To: Class		

Use the words in the box to fill in the chart. Look back at the book report from Mr. Mowse to help you remember what he wrote.

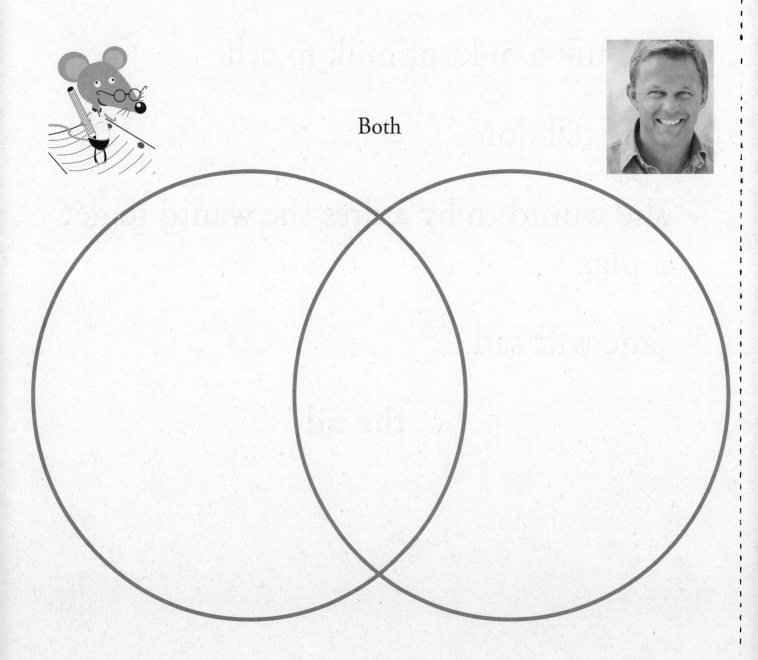

Both

Sound Spellings

This chart lists words with the /ae/ sound spelled four different ways.
Use the chart to fill out Worksheet 5.3.

	'a_e'	'a'	'ai'	'ay'
a	ape	acorn	aim	
b	brake	bacon	bait	bay
c	cake		chain	clay
d	date			day
f	fake		faint	fray
g	gaze	gazing	Gail	gray
h	hate	hating	pain	hay
j	James		jail	Jay
l	late	laser		lay
m	made	making	maid	May
n		naked	nail	
p	plane	paper	plain	pray
r	race	ratings	raisin	ray
s	stake		sail	Sunday
t	take	taking	train	tray
w	wade	waking	wait	way

Sound Spellings

1. Which word on the chart is one of the days of the week?

   _____

2. Which word on the chart names something you write on?

   _____

3. Which two words on the chart are foods?

   _____   _____

4. Can you track down three words that have the suffix *–ing*?

   _____   _____   _____

5. Can you track down two words that sound the same but are not spelled the same way and have a different meaning?

   _____   _____

6. Which word is the name of a nut that falls from a tree?

   _____

7. Which word on the chart is the thing you step on to stop a car?

   _____

Directions: Have students use the chart from Worksheet 5.2 to answer the questions.

8. Can you track down two words that are names?

   _____   _____

9. Which word on the chart is something that you can ride in going down the railroad tracks?

   _____

10. Where is the 'ay' spelling used in words? _____

11. Is the 'ai' spelling used at the end of words? _____

12. Write a sentence using a word from the chart.

   _____

   _____

   _____

   _____

13. Write a sentence using at least two words from the chart.

   _____

   _____

   _____

   _____

Dear Family Member,

    The spelling words for this week include words with tricky spellings for the letters 'c' and 'g'. These letters are tricky because they can be sounded out in different ways. To hear the difference, say the words *got* and *gem*, *cat* and *cents*. Please remember to practice the spelling words for five to ten minutes each night.

    Today your child is also bringing home a story to read, "Miss Baker," and an accompanying worksheet. This is another story in our Unit 3 Reader, *Kids Excel*. You may remember that *Kids Excel* is about kids who are outstanding in different ways. Miss Baker is a teacher who helps a young girl become a good speller. After reading "Miss Baker," have your child answer the story questions on the accompanying worksheet. You should encourage your child to look back at the story to find the answers.

'g'	'c'
page	space
germ	face
digit	cell
gray	center
	carpet

Tricky Word: are

Miss Baker

I was sitting with spelling champ Gail Day.

I asked her, "How did this Miss Baker make you into a good speller?"

"Well," said Gail, "Miss Baker had a cool way of explaining English spelling. She made spelling trees."

"Spelling trees?"

"Yes," said Gail. "Here, I'll make one for you."

Gail got a sheet of paper and made a tree.

She pointed at the trunk of the tree and explained, "The trunk stands for a sound, like the sound /ae/ as in *cake*. The branches stand for the spellings for that sound. There's one branch for words that have the 'a_e' spelling like *flame* and *stake*. There's one branch for words that have the 'ay' spelling like *play* and *stay*. There's one branch for words that have the 'ai' spelling like *pain* and *train*. And so on. Get it?"

"Got it."

"So Miss Baker would make a big spelling tree for a sound. Then we kids would add words to it. When we found words with the sound in them we would stick the words on the branches of the tree. We would stick all of the words with the 'ai' spelling on this branch. We would stick all of the words with the 'ay' spelling on that branch."

"I see. And this helped you get better at spelling?"

Gail nodded.

"The spelling trees helped us see the patterns and keep track of the spellings. They helped us see which spellings are used a lot and which ones are used less. There were a lot of good spellers in Miss Baker's class."

"But not all of them went on to win the state spelling bee," I said. "Why did you?"

Gail shrugged.

"I was good at spelling. But I did not understand why English spelling was so hard. Once I asked Miss Baker why it was so hard. 'Miss Baker,' I said, 'why are there five or six spellings for some sounds? That makes no sense. Why isn't there just one spelling for a sound?'"

Miss Baker explained as much as she could. Then she gave me a book on spelling. It was a cool book. It explained how English has taken in lots of spellings from French, Latin, Greek, and Spanish. When I finished that book, Miss Baker gave me a longer book. Then I found the next book by myself. One book sort of led to the next. So that's how I got started."

Name _____

Miss Baker

Directions: Have your child answer the questions, looking back to the story if necessary. Then have your child complete the Spelling Tree on the back of this worksheet.

1. What did the kids in Miss Baker's class make?

    A. They made spelling bees.

    B. They made spelling trees.

    C. They made spelling lists.

2. What does the trunk of a spelling tree stand for?

    A. The trunk stands for a word.

    B. The trunk stands for a spelling.

    C. The trunk stands for a sound.

3. Leaves with words of the same spelling go on the same _____.

    A. trunk

    B. branch

    C. list

4. Add words to the leaves on the different branches of the
    Spelling Tree.

Yes or No

Directions: Have students answer yes or no to the questions. On the last two lines, have students create their own questions.

1. Can a dog shake its tail?   _____

2. Can a raisin sing?   _____

3. Do airplanes eat hay?   _____

4. Can you braid your hair?   _____

5. Does three make a pair?   _____

6. Are acorns from trees?   _____

7. Do cakes sleep in parks?   _____

8. Can you race a horse?   _____

9. Do you have fingernails?   _____

10. Can you make a sad face? _____

11. Can a rake shake a leg? _____

12. Do books have pages? _____

13. Can a crayon smile? _____

14. Is Sunday a day in the weekend? _____

15. Can you read a tale? _____

16. Can you use a rake to sweep
    leaves into a pile? _____

17. _____

18. _____

Same or Different

Directions: Have students first circle the spelling for the vowel sound and then read each word. They should write yes if the words have the same vowel sound, and no if they do not.

	Word 1	Word 2	Are the sounds the same?
	train	track	No
1.	cap	cape	
2.	wag	wade	
3.	rate	rain	
4.	stake	wait	
5.	sand	sad	
6.	hate	hat	
7.	paid	paper	
8.	faint	play	
9.	pat	pay	

Word 1	Word 2	Are the sounds the same?
10. shave	faint	
11. pain	pan	
12. chain	chat	
13. stay	stain	
14. hay	hat	
15. plate	pain	
16. flag	flat	
17. fat	fate	
18. aim	am	

Spelling Sort

Sort the words by their spellings. Write the words with the /oe/ sound spelled 'oa' under *load*, the words with the /oe/ sound spelled 'oe' under *doe*, and the words with the /oe/ sound spelled 'o_e' under *home*.

toes	choke	boat	goes	coat
hoe	tote	coast	foe	toenail
tiptoe	Joe	road	vote	coach
poke	doze	loading	float	hope

/oe/ spelled 'oa' as in *load*	/oe/ spelled 'oe' as in *doe*	/oe/ spelled 'o_e' as in *home*
	toes	
_____	_____	_____
_____	_____	_____
_____	_____	_____
_____	_____	_____
_____	_____	_____
_____	_____	_____
_____	_____	_____

1. _____

2. _____

3. _____

Directions: Have students sort the words by sounds and write three sentences using words from the box. After students write each word, they will circle the /oe/ spelling in each word.

1. The (baker) made a (cake) at his (shop)   (3)

2. The boy had a big book.   (2)

3. The man was waxing the car at home.   (3)

4. Kids ride bikes to the park.   (3)

5. The storm made the tree shake.   (2)

person	place	thing
baker	shop	cake

Directions: Have students circle the nouns in each sentence. After circling each noun, have students write the word on the lines below before going to the next noun. Note: the number of nouns in each sentence is written at the end of the sentence.

© 2013 Core Knowledge Foundation

Dear Family Member,

The words shown below contain the /oe/ sound (*road, toes, stroke*) and the /o/ sound (*hot, top*, etc.). Have your child read the words and tally how many times the spelling occurs in the boxes below. If you have time, also ask your child to use each word in a complete sentence.

toast	stroke	shopper	goes	coat
road	robber	loan	stone	home
foal	soap	toes	toad	oats
boat	shot	cot	coal	chomp
Rome	Joe	foe	goal	pose

'o_e' (*hope*)	
'oe' (*hoe*)	
'oa' (*boat*)	
'o' (*hop*)	

Spelling Sort

Sort the words by spelling. Write the words with the /oe/ sound spelled 'o' under *go*, the words with the /oe/ sound spelled 'oa' under *foal*, the words with the /oe/ sound spelled 'oe' under *toe*, and the words with the /oe/ sound spelled 'o_e' under *bone*.

bone	go	foal	toe
rope	soap	doe	note
home	hole	choke	Joe
over	focus	donate	coat
coal	opened	moment	load
provide	robot	floating	mole

'o'	'oa'	'oe'	'o_e'
go	**foal**	**toe**	**bone**
_____	_____	_____	_____
_____	_____	_____	_____
_____	_____	_____	_____
_____	_____	_____	_____
_____	_____	_____	_____
_____	_____	_____	_____

50 Free	500 Free	200 Free
faster sprints	faster in long races	100 Free

Directions: Use the words in the box to fill in the chart.

Kim   Kim and Val   Val

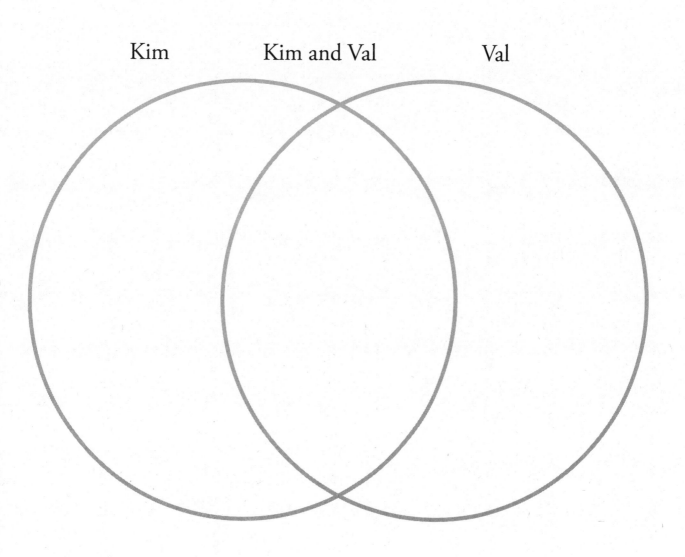

The Swimming Sisters

Kim and Val Castro are swimming sisters.

Kim is sixteen. Val is fifteen. The sisters swim
for the Red River Swim Program (RRSP). Both of them are fast.
In fact, they are two of the fastest swimmers in the state.

I went to see the two sisters at the pool where they swim. They
were training for a big meet.

"So," I said, "do I dare ask which of you is faster?"

Kim smiled. "I am faster in the sprints," she said. "But Val is
faster in the long races."

"So what counts as a sprint in swimming?"

"The 50 Free is a sprint," said Kim.

"50?" I said. "Is that 50 feet?"

"No," said Kim, "it's 50 yards."

"Gosh!" I said. "50 yards? That's a sprint? It sounds long to me!
You see, I am not much of a swimmer."

"The 50 Free is an all-out sprint," Kim said. "It's like the
hundred yard dash in track. It's over in a flash. The 100 Free is a
sprint, too."

"So what counts as a long race in swimming?"

"The 500 Free is a long race," Kim groaned. "It's too long
for me. I start to get tired after 150 yards or so. But not Val! The
longer the race is, the better she is."

"The 500 Free is my best race!" said Val.

"500 yards?" I said. "What's that, a hundred laps?"

"Um, no," Val said. "In a 25-yard pool, it's up and back ten times."

I jotted notes in my notebook.

"So let's see," I said. "100 yards counts as a short race. Kim is good at the short races. 500 yards is a long race. Val is good at the long races. Is there a race that is longer than 100 yards and shorter than 500?"

"Yes, there is," said Kim. "The 200 Free."

"So which of you speedsters wins that race?" I asked.

Kim looked at Val. She had a smile on her face. It was a sister-to-sister smile, and there was something else in it. There was a sort of challenge in the look.

Val smiled back. She had the same look on her face.

I waited.

At last Kim spoke. "It's hard to say who is faster in the 200 Free. Sometimes Val wins and sometimes I win."

"I see," I said. "It sounds like the 200 Free is the race to see. When will that race take place?"

"It will be on Sunday," said Val, "the last day of the state meet."

I got out my pen and wrote: "Sunday the 25th. 200 Free. Castro versus Castro!"

The Swimming Sisters

1. In what sport do Kim and Val Castro excel?

    A. They excel at spelling.

    B. They excel at swimming.

    C. They excel at running.

2. Which sister is faster in sprint races, Kim or Val?

    A. Kim is faster than Val.

    B. Val is faster than Kim.

3. How old is Kim?_____

4. How old is Val?_____

Directions: Have your child answer the questions after reading the story. Remind him/her to look back at the story to find the answers, and write in complete sentences.

5. Which sister do you think will win the 200 Free in the big meet? Why?

_____

_____

_____

_____

_____

_____

6. List six nouns used in "The Swimming Sisters."

_____   _____

_____   _____

_____   _____

Making Words

Directions: Have students combine two of the three syllables to create a word that completes the sentence and write the word on the line provided.

1.   king   po   smo

a) One thing that is bad for your lungs is _____.

b) Beth was reading until Sam started _____ her.

2.   ver   o   kay

a) The airplane zoomed _____ our house.

b) I was sick yesterday, but this morning I feel _____.

3.   ro   dents   bot

a) The _____ made beeping noises.

b) Rats, mice, and voles are all _____.

4.   tect   gram   pro

a) The TV _____ begins at six o'clock.

b) The firemen will _____ us from the fire.

5.   sol   id   rap

a) The ice was frozen _____.

b) A plane is faster and more _____ than a bike.

6. My teacher is Po lish. / Pol ish.

7. My mom asked me to po lish / pol ish the desk.

8. Dan likes to collect mo del / mod el cars

9. Mr. Chang is the gro cer / groc er at the corner store.

10. The chairs were made of so lid / sol id oak wood.

Spelling Test

1. _____

2. _____

3. _____

4. _____

5. _____

6. _____

7. _____

8. _____

9. _____

10. _____

 _____

_____

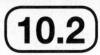
Sound Spellings

This chart lists words with the /oe/ sound spelled four different ways. Use the chart to fill out Worksheet 10.3.

	'o_e'	'o'	'oa'	'oe'
b	bone	bonus	boast	
c	close	cola	coach	
d	dope	donate		doe
f		frozen	foam	
g		going	groan	goes
h	home	halo		hoe
j	joke	jumbo		Joe
l	lone	locate	loaf	
			loan	
m	mope	moment	moan	mangoes
n	note			
o		open	oatmeal	
p		program		
r	rode	robot	road	
s	slope	solo	soap	
t	tone		toad	toes
			toast	
w	wrote			

Use the chart on Worksheet 10.2 to fill in the blanks.

1. Which word means the same thing as a "deer?" _____

2. Which word on the chart is stuff you use to get clean when you take a shower? _____

3. Write three foods listed on the chart.

    _____   _____   _____

4. Which words sound the same, but are not spelled the same?

    _____   _____

5. Which word means extra large? _____

6. Which word on the chart names things that are on your feet?

    _____

7. Which word on the chart names something that is a lot like a frog? _____

8. Which word on the chart is a man's name? _____

9. Which word on the chart names a tool farmers use to dig up the ground? _____

BONUS:

1. Count the words on the chart having the sound /oe/ spelled 'o_e' and write the number here. _____

2. Count the words on the chart having the sound /oe/ spelled 'o' and write the number here. _____

3. Count the words on the chart having the sound /oe/ spelled 'oa' and write the number here. _____

4. Count the words on the chart having the sound /oe/ spelled 'oe' and write the number here. _____

Dear Family Member,

The spelling words for this week include the spelling alternatives 'kn', 'wr', 'wh', 'qu' at the beginning of the words and the suffixes *–ing* and *–ed*. These words are challenging because students may try to spell them with more common spellings. For example, they might want to spell *whipped* as *wipped*, or *knotted* as *notted*. Please remember to practice the spelling words for five to ten minutes each night.

'kn'	**'wr'**	**'wh'**	**'qu'**
knotted	wringing	whipped	quitting
knitting	wronged	whined	quacked
knocked			

Tricky Word: all

Fill in the Blank

angel	explain	solar	cockroach	entire	panel
yesterday	halo	explode	invite	umpire	

1. The _____ said the batter was out!

2. I asked the teacher to _____ the math problem.

3. If today is Sunday, what day was it _____?

4. Let's _____ Ted and Carl to dinner.

5. A _____ is an insect.

6. Mister Smith drank so much cola, he said he felt as if he would
    _____.

7. The _____ _____ on the roof
    heats the house.

8. There is a _____ over the head of the
    _____.

9. Sam ate the _____ cake.

Directions: Have students complete the sentence with one of the words from the box.

Fill in the Blank

| fried | reptiles | umpire | lie | siren | tie |
| cried | spider | exercise | pie | pilot | decide |

1. The airplane _____ said we were going to take off.

2. At the game, the _____ said the player was out.

3. Please _____ a strong knot in the string on the kite.

4. A _____ has 8 legs and can weave a web.

5. I like to eat _____ after dinner.

6. My Grandpa is scared of _____ like snakes.

7. I cannot tell a _____!

8. He fell and _____.

9. Did you _____ what to wear today?

10. We had _____ chicken for dinner.

11. My dad likes to jog in the morning for _____.

12. A fire truck has a loud _____.

Number the events in the order in which they happened.

_____ The swimmers shot off.

_____ Val was the winner!

_____ A man's booming voice filled the air.

_____ Mark got to the pool in time for the 200 Free.

_____ Kim was starting to look tired.

_____ The man started listing the swimmers.

Grammar

1. the   man   has   a   shop   on   pike   street   (4)

    The man has a shop on Pike Street.

    _____

2. will   jan   help   mom   make   cupcakes   sunday   (4)

    _____

    _____

3. kim   will   be   nine   in   may   (2)

    _____

    _____

4. gail   got   the   mail   on   fern   street   (4)

    _____

    _____

5. josh took bait on his fishing trip

    to drake lake (5)

    _____

    _____

6. did trish let her pal ride on her bike (3)

    _____

    _____

Sound Spellings

This chart lists the words with the /ie/ sound spelled three different ways. Use this chart to fill out Worksheet 13.2.

	'i_e'	'ie'	'i'
b	bike		bicep
c	crime		cider
d	dine	die	diner
f	fine		finest
h	hide		hijack
i	ice		iris
k	knife		
l	like	lie	lilac
m	mice		mining
p	prize	pie	
q	quite		quiet
r	ride		riding
s	side		silent
	smile		spider
t	time	tie	tiger
v	vine		Viking
w	write		writing

Sound Spellings

Directions: Have students use the chart on Worksheet 13.1 to answer the questions.

1. Which word on the chart is something you do when you are glad? _____

2. Which two words on the chart means there is no sound? _____ _____

3. Which word on the chart is something that you place in a drink to make it cooler? _____

4. Which word on the chart has two wheels?_____

5. Which word on the chart is a plant that has grapes? _____

6. Which word on the chart is an animal that growls? _____

7. Which word on the chart is the name of a place you could go to eat lunch or dinner? _____

8. Can you track down three words that end with /ie/? _____ _____ _____

9. Count the words on the chart having the sound /ie/ spelled 'i_e' and write the number here.

   _____

10. Count the words on the chart having the sound /ie/ spelled 'ie' and write the number here.

    _____

11. Count the words on the chart having the sound /ie/ spelled 'i' and write the number here.

    _____

S T A R T

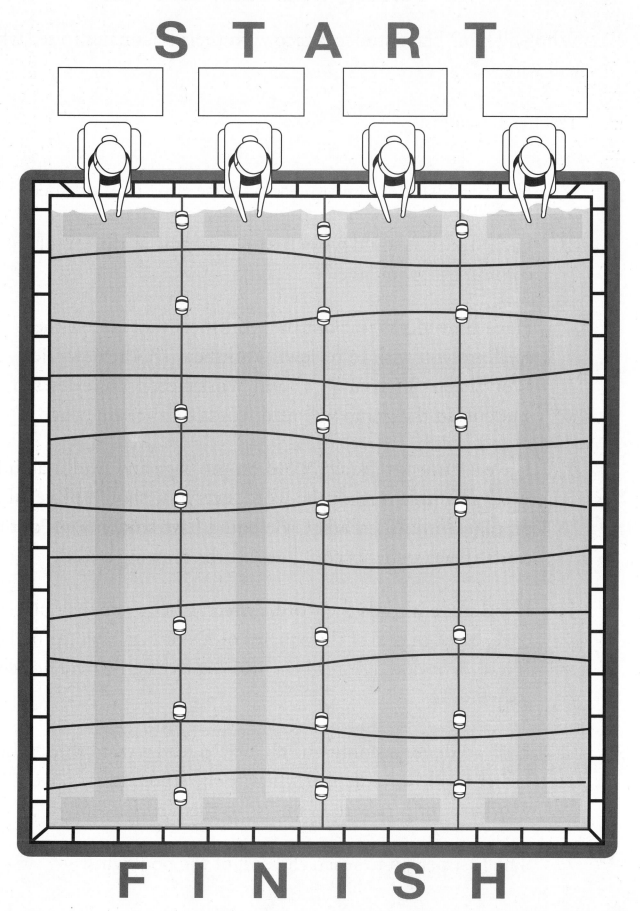

F I N I S H

Racing with Kim and Val!

Who will win? Have students race with their classmates to see who will win.

Teacher Directions:

1. Have each student group tear out one copy of Worksheet 13.3.

2. Each student should write his or her name at the top of a column or "swim lane."

3. Have all students tear out the worksheet that targets the spellings you wish to review: Worksheet 13.4 reviews /ie/, Worksheet 13.5 reviews 'a', and Worksheet 13.6 reviews 'o'. All students in the group will read words on the same page.

4. Have a student pick any word on the page and read it aloud. After the student reads the word, everyone should place an X on that word. Alternately, you could have students cut out the cards. Then students could take turns drawing a card.

5. If the student reads the word correctly, he or she may place a checkmark in one of the squares of his or her "swimming lane." If a student does not read the word correctly, he may not check a square.

6. Each student gets only one chance to read a word during his or her turn. Regardless of whether the student reads his or her word correctly, play then moves to the next student.

7. The first person to reach the end of the pool wins!

Game Cards: Focus Spelling 'i'

life	price	visit	spider
dining	quiet	timeline	siren
river	lifetime	limestone	igloo
bridesmaid	limit	pinecone	hippo
spine	minus	bidding	sliding
wisecrack	singing	linebacker	lining
Viking	tide	grapevine	pie
lipstick	sideline	bitesize	ping-pong
hi	sister	die	bedtime
item	silent	winter	wishbone
lie	slime	milestone	pipeline

Game Cards: Focus Spelling 'a'

mermaid	at	may	cap
paper	fat	danish	pain
cake	rainstorm	taper	naptime
ray	wager	crab	rapping
train	caper	painter	stay
acorn	ape	lapping	mail
pray	batboy	daytime	basic
faking	subway	baking	batting
snail	grade	wait	hayride
waving	hag	play	mapping
snapped	yesterday	grab	payment

Game Cards: Focus Spelling 'o'

frozen	possum	omit	robber
poker	soon	robot	bonus
tadpole	oatmeal	woeful	comment
explode	sailboat	spoon	halo
omit	oboe	over	locate
hippo	raccoon	moment	hotel
slope	raincoat	goat	copper
rope	polo	open	hoedown
spoke	stone	poem	soap
rosebud	roadway	bathrobe	stepmom
without	toes	lobster	comet

The Big Race

I got to the pool in time for the 200 Free. I sat in the stands with Grover and Joan Castro, Kim and Val's parents.

"I am so proud of Kim and Val," said Grover Castro. "But I have a bad case of nerves. I hate it when the two of them swim in the same race. They have both been training so hard. They would both like to win this race. But they can't both win. I don't like to think that one of them may be upset."

A man's booming voice filled the air. "It's time for the last race of the meet!" the man said.

"Let's meet our swimmers!" The man started listing the swimmers in the race.

"In Lane 2," he said, "from Red River Swim Program, we have the winner of the 500 Free, Val Castro." Cheers rose up from the RRSP swimmers on the deck and from fans in the stands.

"In Lane 3," the man said, "from Red River Swim Program, the winner of the 50 and 100 Free, Kim Castro." There were shouts and cheers for Kim, as well.

The swimmers got up on the starting blocks.

A man in a white coat said, "Swimmers, take your marks." The swimmers bent down and grabbed the starting blocks.

Then there was a beep. The swimmers shot off. Kim's start was perfect. She did her kick. Then she popped up and started swimming. Her arms went so fast. She seemed to be coasting.

Kim was the fastest swimmer for a hundred yards. She made a big wave. The rest of the swimmers were trailing her. They seemed to be bouncing and sloshing in Kim's waves.

I was starting to think it would not be such a close race after all. But just as I was thinking this, Grover Castro said, "Wait for it!"

"Wait for what?" I said.

"You'll see!" said Grover.

I looked back at the pool. Kim was still winning. But Val was closing in on her. The gap was five feet. Then it was three.

The swimmers flipped one last time. Kim was starting to look a bit tired. The gap was down to two feet. Then it was one foot. Then the two sisters were swimming side by side. As they came to the finish line it was too close to pick a winner. Kim and Val smacked the side of the pool at what looked to be the same moment.

A hundred parents in the stands looked up at the clock. A hundred swimmers on the deck looked up as well.

This is what the clock said:

| Val Castro | Lane 2 | 1:45 |
| Kim Castro | Lane 3 | 1:46 |

Val was the winner!

The Big Race

Directions: Have your child answer the questions after reading the story. Remind them to look back at the story to find the answers, and to write in complete sentences.

1. Who are Grover and Joan Castro?

   A. Grover and Joan Castro are fast swimmers.

   B. Grover and Joan Castro are pals of Mark Deeds.

   C. Grover and Joan Castro are Kim and Val's parents.

2. What makes Grover Castro have a bad case of nerves?

   A. He doesn't like to go to swim meets.

   B. He ate something that made him sick.

   C. He doesn't like it when Kim and Val are in the same race.

3. Which swimmer was in Lane 3?

   A. Kim was in Lane 3.

   B. Val was in Lane 3.

4. Which swimmer had a perfect start?

   A. Kim had a perfect start.

   B. Val had a perfect start.

5. Which sister was the fastest swimmer for a hundred yards?

   A. Kim was the fastest swimmer for a hundred yards.

   B. Val was the fastest swimmer for a hundred yards.

6. Which sister was the winner at the end of the race?

    A.   Kim was the winner.

    B.   Val was the winner.

7. Who did you think would win the race? Why?

_____

_____

_____

_____

Grammar

Directions: Have students rewrite the sentences with correct punctuation and capitalization. They should box the common nouns and circle the proper nouns.

1. beth and i had to switch places for the game

   _____

   _____

2. i am making a paper plane, said david

   _____

   _____

3. jean said, i hope i am not late for snacks

   _____

   _____

4. today is monday august 22, 2010

   _____

   _____

5. would you like to go to jones park

   _____

   _____

boy

beth

1. jane

2. shop

3. main street

4. game

5. sam

6. desk

7. day

8. mike

9. coach

10. sunday

11. october

12. park

common noun

Beth

_____

_____

_____

_____

_____

_____

_____

_____

_____

_____

_____

_____

Part I

1. man   _____**Dan**_____

2. street   _____

3. teacher   _____

4. town   _____

5. state   _____

6. day   _____

7. boy   _____

8. shop   _____

Part II

common noun (thing)	common noun (place)	common noun (person)
fork	**kitchen**	**man**
_____	_____	_____

Directions: Part I: Ask your child to write one proper noun for each common noun. Part II: Ask your child to look around at home and find one noun for each of the three categories. Part III: Tell your child to look around at home and find a total of five objects or people that are proper nouns.

Part III

Example: _____ **Tyler** _____

1. _____

2. _____

3. _____

4. _____

5. _____

Spelling Test

1. _____

2. _____

3. _____

4. _____

5. _____

6. _____

7. _____

8. _____

9. _____

10. _____

 _____

_____

Plurals

Look at each picture. Write the name of each picture correctly on the line.

Directions: Have students look at each picture and write the word correctly on the line.

dishes

_____

_____

_____

_____

_____

_____

_____

_____

_____

_____

_____

1. playground   playtime   plaything   placemat

2. translate   transfer   lake   later

3. magic   matter   magnet   maintain

4. lard   late   lap   lapping

5. plan   pain   painter   plain

6. tiptoe   toenail   tipping   tipped

7. joshing   jeering   joking   jerking

8. diner   dined   dimmer   dinner

9. swimming   smelling   smiling   smiled

10. slim   slimmer   slime   lime

11. mayday   mayhem   maybe   may

12. remit   remote   remain   remake

13. silver   sail   slime   silent

14. raise   raisin   rays   razor

15. roach   reach   wrote   road

16. doe   do   dine   dope

17. quilt   quoted   quill   quiet

18. team   tired   tied   timed

19. gripping   griped   grip   gripe

20. Friday   fine   finish   farmer

Dear Family Member,

Our spelling words this week are antonyms and synonyms. Antonyms are words that mean the opposite. For example, *cold* is an antonym of *hot*. Synonyms are words that have almost the same meaning. *Cool* is a synonym for *cold*. You can practice with your child in this way: say the italicized word and ask your child to think of the word that is a synonym or antonym for that word and write it down. For example:

You say, "Write the antonym for *over*." Then your child should say and then write the word *under* on his/her paper. Remember, in addition to practicing spelling words, it is a great benefit for students to read at least 20 minutes every night.

Spelling Word	Antonym
under	*over*
noise	*silence*
open	*close*
brave	*scared*
cute	*ugly*

Spelling Word	Synonym
minus	*subtract*
last	*final*
foe	*rival*
robber	*bandit*
road	*street*

No Tricky Word this week

Fill In The Blank

Fill in the blank with a word from the box.

cute	huge	confused	refused
fumes	compute	accused	mute

1. There is too much noise. Please put the TV on
   _____.

2. If there is a gas leak, you will smell _____.

3. In math class, we learn how to _____.

4. The power went off in the _____ storm.

5. I asked to stay up later, but my mom _____ and
   said it was time for bed.

6. I still felt _____ even after the teacher explained
   how to do the worksheet.

7. Pam said my dress was _____.

8. The robber was _____ of stealing cash from the
   bank.

Name _____

Write an antonym on the line.

1. open _____

2. add _____

3. up _____

4. sad _____

5. sour _____

Write a synonym on the line.

1. enjoy _____

2. large _____

3. lawn _____

4. quick _____

5. moist _____

Fill in the Blank

Fill in the blank with a word from the box.

barbecued	unicorn	argue	argument	using
fuel	menu	unit	United	

1. A _____ has a horn between its ears.

2. We will be _____ pens today.

3. Our _____ in math is on adding two numbers.

4. I had an _____ with my mom about what I would wear today.

5. I don't like to _____ with my mom.

6. What is on the _____ for lunch today?

7. We are in the _____ States of America.

8. Dad stopped to get _____ for the car.

9. I like to eat _____ chicken.

1. That (man) drives those (cars) fast. (2 nouns)

2. The boats race at the lake. (2 nouns)

3. My pal got two cute dresses. (2 nouns)

4. Did Beth write the notes? (2 nouns)

5. wish _____

6. boat _____

7. box _____

8. sandwich _____

9. boss _____

Directions: For numbers 1–4, have students circle the nouns in each sentence. Above each noun, write an "S" if the noun is singular or write a "P" if the noun is plural. For numbers 5–9, write the plural form for each word. Remind students to be sure to look at the ending of each word carefully.

Plurals

| glass ~~glass~~ | patch | trip | rash | box | sock | mess |

Add –s	Add –es
	glasses

Sound Spellings

This chart shows spellings for the /ue/ sound. Use the chart to fill in
Worksheet 18.2.

	'u_e'	'u'	'ue'
a		argument	argue
b			barbecue
c	confuse cube cute		cue
f	fumes fuse		fuel
h		humid	hue
j	June		
m	mule mute	menu music	
p	pure	pupil	
r	refuse	refusing	rescue
t		tulip	
u	use	using unicorn uniform	
v			value

Sound Spellings

Use the chart on Worksheet 18.1 to fill in the blanks.

1. Which spelling for /ue/ is the least common?

    _____

2. Where does the spelling 'ue' tend to be found in a word?

    _____

3. Which word in the chart is the name of a flower?

    _____

4. What word in the chart is a shape that looks like a box or square?

    _____

5. What word in the chart is the name of something you would use at a diner to order lunch?

    _____

6. What word on the chart means to cook on a grill outside?

   _____

7. Pick a word from the chart that can be used as a verb. Write a sentence that uses that verb.

   _____

   _____

8. Pick a word from the chart that can be used as a noun. Write a sentence using that noun.

   _____

   _____

Sunshine the Mule

START

END

Help Farmer Chester Get Sunshine the Mule Back to the Barn!

Farmer Chester is in a fix. Sunshine the Mule has escaped from the barn again! Help Farmer Chester get Sunshine to the barn.

Teacher Directions:

1. Group students in pairs or small groups to play. Each player should tear out a game sheet (Worksheet 18.3).

2. Tell students to turn to Worksheets 18.4 and 18.5.

3. Explain that the first student should choose and read any "card" on the page. After the student reads the card, all players should cross out the card on their own page.

4. If the student reads the card correctly, he or she may place a checkmark on one space of his or her own game board. If the student can also answer the question correctly, he or she may place another checkmark on another space on the game board.

5. After the first student finishes his or her turn, the other player(s) should take a turn.

6. The first player to lead Sunshine back to the barn wins.

Name _____

18.4

Help Farmer Chester Get Sunshine the Mule Back to the Barn!

Would you kiss a mule?	Do you add in a math unit?	Can corn on the cob rescue you?
Is a unicorn real?	Are we in the United States?	Should you argue with your mom?
Is the moon red?	Does a unicorn have 3 horns?	Do mules wear uniforms?
Can a mule sing a song?	Can a boy be named Sue?	Do you eat bacon in the bathtub?
Can you place mail in a mailbox?	Can you read a menu at a diner?	If you are seen in public, are you hiding?
Can a cucumber play a song?	Is a tulip a sort of food?	Can it be humid on a hot summer day?
Can a cute cat pat a dog?	Can a unicorn use a crayon?	Can you argue with a spider?
Can you write with a pencil on paper?	Are you using your brain?	Can you eat corn on a cob?

Unit 3 **115**
© 2013 Core Knowledge Foundation

Would you use a stick to cut a slice of cake?	Can a mule point to a book?	Could a powerful king wear a crown?
Can you cook an ice cube?	Can a cow be rescued by an ant?	Can you play music with an ice cube?
Can a mouse count out loud?	Could a huge eggplant be in a garden?	Could you hear the TV if it is on mute?
Can a TV dance in a garden?	Can you eat a cube of fudge?	Would an ice cube start a fire?
Can you eat a raisin?	Would a dog rescue a shark?	Would a cube of ice be a good snack?
If your book is overdue, do you have to pay a fine?	Can you act sad?	Can a mule dance a jig?
Are you a cube?	Have you patted a unicorn?	Can you knit a set of books?
Can you dance to the music?	Can beans have three wheels?	Are you a duck?

Write at least 5 adjectives describing the jumper of your choice.

Jumper _____

1. _____

2. _____

3. _____

4. _____

5. _____

Antonyms

1. up _____

2. over _____

3. inside _____

4. open _____

5. ask _____

6. whisper _____

7. start _____

8. yes _____

9. on _____

10. bad _____

Directions: Have your child write an antonym beside each word.

Synonyms

1. finish _____

2. child _____

3. hope _____

4. jump _____

5. shout _____

6. moist _____

7. silent _____

8. toad _____

9. sweet _____

10. up _____

Directions: Have your child write a synonym beside each word.

Use the words for the crossword puzzle.

paw	claw	August	author	faucet
saucepan	Claus	pause	lawn	Autumn

Side-to-side

2.   Summer, _____, Winter, Spring

4.   This is at the sink.

7.   The cat's _____ is cut.

9.   You cook in this.

Down

1.   _____, September, October

3.   The tiger's _____ is sharp.

5.   Santa _____

6.   You cut the grass on the _____.

8.   An _____ writes a book.

10. This is a short break.

Name _____

© 2013 Core Knowledge Foundation

Jump!

Directions: Have students answer the questions.

1. What is the setting of "Jump!"?

    A. The setting is on a lawn.

    B. The setting is on a playground.

    C. The setting is in a graveyard.

    Page _____

2. What is the name of the jump rope team?

    A. The name of the team is the Jumping Beans.

    B. The name of the team is the Joking Stars.

    C. The name of the team is the Jumping Stars.

    Page _____

3. What makes jumping rope a sport?

    A. The team performs jokes.

    B. The team performs plays.

    C. The team performs tricks.

    Page _____

4. How fast is the jump rope spinning?

    A. The rope does not spin too fast so the team can do tricks.

    B. The rope spins so fast you can hardly see it.

    C. The rope spins as fast as a tree falling.

    Page _____

5. What is the name of the new trick that Jo made up?

    A.   The trick is named the flip.

    B.   The trick is named the jump.

    C.   The trick is named the hop.

    Page _____

6. How did the team finish last time?

    _____

    _____

    _____

    Page _____

7. What does the word *nail* mean in this sentence, "We need to get to the point where we *nail* it nine times out of ten."

    A.   In this sentence, nail means to get it perfect.

    B.   In this sentence, nail means to hammer it.

    C.   In this sentence, nail means to hit it hard.

    Page _____

Spelling Test

1. _____

2. _____

3. _____

4. _____

5. _____

6. _____

7. _____

8. _____

9. _____

10. _____

 _____

_____

Write at least 5 sentences for the profile of the jumper of your choice.

Jumper _____

1. _____

2. _____

3. _____

4. _____

5. _____

Yes or No?

1.   Can you applaud after a play? _____

2.   Does an author draw the different parts of a book? _____

3.   Can a dump truck haul rocks? _____

4.   Could a fisherman tell a tale about a fish he caught? _____

5.   Could you help a dog with a thorn in his paw? _____

6.   Has your teacher taught you how to write? _____

7.   Does the exhaust from a bus smell like peaches? _____

8.   Can you launch a pumpkin? _____

Directions: Have students write yes or no to answer each question.

9. Do ice cubes make drinks cool? _____

10. Could there be a tiger on your lawn? _____

11. Can a faucet drip? _____

12. Could you pause to look at the sunset? _____

13. Is it good to get in an argument with your sister? _____

14. Would a mule drink from a straw? _____

15. Could a shark bite with the teeth in his jaws? _____

The Big Storm

Last winter, we got stuck in a big ice storm. The sleet started to come down at noon. When Mom and Dad picked me up at three, sleet was on the ground and on the roads.

We started to drive home. That was when things got exciting. The sleet started coming down harder and harder. It got deeper and deeper. The car started slipping and sliding. I was scared. Dad had to creep along and so did lots of other cars. Then, the cars stopped and there was a big traffic jam. Mom got out and looked down the road to see if cars were moving at all. No one was moving!

We had just passed the road to my granddad's house. Mom called my granddad and asked if we could come and visit. He said we could. So Dad drove to my granddad's house. It took us a long time to get there. There was so much ice that we couldn't see the road! We ended up sleeping at my granddad's house and waiting until the state trucks came and plowed the roads. We had fun being iced in!

Cupcakes with Mom

Last week, I made cupcakes with Mom. We went to the shop to pick up the items we needed for the cupcakes. We got frosting and cake mix. We got cooking oil and eggs.

When we got home, we unpacked our bags and switched on the oven. Mom got out a mixing dish and a spoon. I dumped the cake mix in the dish. Mom let me add the oil and two eggs. I mixed everything together. Mom added paper liners to the cupcake pan. Then I got a spoon and scooped the batter into the cupcake liners. Mom set the timer for the cupcakes to bake in the oven.

Waiting for the cupcakes to cook was the hardest part. It took so long! I kept checking on the cupcakes. At last, the timer started beeping. I jumped up and down and shouted, "Cupcakes! Cupcakes!" Mom got mitts and pulled out the hot pan. The sweet smell of fresh baked cupcakes filled the kitchen. Mom and I put sweet, pink frosting on the cupcakes. I got frosting on my fingers and licked it off. Then Mom and I each chose a cupcake to eat. Yum, yum! Those were the best cupcakes!

Title:

Characters

Setting

Plot

Beginning

Middle

End

Dear Family Member,

This week we will be writing personal narratives. Students will go through the entire writing process, from planning to editing. We will begin with writing a class narrative and then the students will write their own narrative with a partner.

We will finish our current reading unit this Friday and will have several assessments to make sure students have learned the skills in this unit.

For this reason, your child will not have spelling words or a test this week. Students will have homework each night to prepare them for the unit assessments. As this is review work, they should be able to complete the homework independently. Please assist your child in completing the homework only if necessary.

Continue to read with your child each night. You will be surprised by how fast your child will progress if he or she reads aloud to you 20 minutes every night. Be aware that this reading does not have to be a book; it can be labels of cans that you have in the cupboard or cereal boxes or comics! Nor does the reading have to take place at home; it can take place in the car or standing in line at the grocery store.

As always, if you have questions, feel free to contact me. When home and school work together as a team, your child wins!

Name _____

Fill in the Blank

Write a word from the box in the sentence.

globe	coach	goal	chose	cone
grade	train	name	may	mail

1. My sister's _____ is Jane.

2. We have a _____ in our classroom.

3. I am in first _____.

4. Mom's shaved ice _____ has melted.

5. I _____ the dress I wanted to wear today
    before going to bed.

6. _____ I have a snack?

7. Place the letter in the _____ box.

8. Our team needs a _____.

9. The soccer player made a _____.

10. What time will the _____ get here?

© 2013 Core Knowledge Foundation

© 2013 Core Knowledge Foundation

Grammar

1. The (cars) will crash. (1)

2. The desk broke. (1)

3. The firemen wear coats like raincoats. (3)

4. Dad drives us to the playground. (2)

5. Five foxes ran by the road. (2)

6. James shouts for help. (2)

7. Kim skipped down the hill. (2)

8. The class played soccer. (2)

9. The boys drank cola. (2)

10. Sam ate mangoes. (2)

11. The kids jumped rope. (2)

Title:

Characters

Setting

Plot

Beginning

Middle

End

Dear Family Member,

Our class has been working on writing personal narratives at school. Your child has read personal narratives, and we have drafted a personal narrative as a class. Now, each student will have an opportunity to write his or her own personal narrative describing something that happened to him or her. As homework, please work with your child to brainstorm ideas that he or she might write about in a personal narrative. Remind your child that the personal narrative is nonfiction; it should tell about something that really happened to him or her. Here are some ideas for topics your child might be interested in writing about:

- a special holiday or birthday

- a special present they received

- something a friend or sibling did for them

- a special visit or a trip to an interesting place

- a "first" or significant personal achievement

- a weather-related event

Have your child jot down ideas on the back of this page.

Personal Narrative Ideas

*

*

*

*

*

Verbs

Directions: Have students read the words in each row. Draw a squiggly line under the word in each row that is an action verb.

1. street   foxes   pinches   lake

2. blanket   runs   swimmer   road

3. leaf   whale   cleans   number

4. Spain   picnic   digs   unicorn

5. raced   house   artist   bathtub

Write a sentence using a noun and verb from the list.

1. _____

2. _____

3. _____

4. _____

5. _____

Title:

Characters

Setting

Plot

Beginning

Middle

End

Writing Sentences

rice	tie	silent	cider	tiger
use	unit	mule	rescue	cute

Directions: Have your child read all the words in the box and use any five of the words from the box to write five sentences.

1. _____

   _____

2. _____

   _____

3. _____

   _____

4. _____

   _____

5. _____

   _____

Editing Checklist

Ask yourself these questions as you edit your draft.

1. Do I have a title?	
2. Have I described the setting at the start?	
3. Have I named and described the characters?	
4. Do I have a plot with • a beginning? • a middle? • an end?	
5. Do all of my sentences start with uppercase letters?	
6. Do all of my sentences end with a final mark? (. ? or !)	
7. Have I spelled all of my words correctly?	
8. Have I added "sense" words that describe how things look, feel, taste, sound, or smell?	

Writing Sentences

Use any five of the words from the box to write five sentences.

August	thaw	paws	daughter	taught
draw	saw	fault	law	applaud

1. _____

_____

2. _____

_____

3. _____

_____

4. _____

_____

5. _____

_____

1. goes   gaze   go   Gus

2. bake   brook   beach   beat

3. sell   sauce   shawl   saw

4. caught   cup   cue   cute

5. taught   coat   caught   daughter

6. wait   white   wade   way

7. best   boast   boat   bones

8. fraud   freed   fray   frame

9. fail   fray   frail   fame

10. hail   hill   hay   heat

11. thaw   than   teach   taught

12. pale   pile   pilot   pills

13. music   muse   mute   mud

14. place   pup   puppet   pupil

The Splash Artist

1. Why is Jethro Otter called *The Splash Artist?*

   A. He can make a big splash.

   B. He can paint splashes.

   C. He can target his splashes.

2. Who named Jethro *The Splash Artist?*

   A. Jethro's mom named him *The Splash Artist.*

   B. Jethro's sisters named him *The Splash Artist.*

   C. Jethro's dad named him *The Splash Artist.*

3. What did Jethro's dad do while Jethro was getting on his swim trunks?

   A. Dad pointed out the pool to Mark Deeds.

   B. Dad pointed out the house to Mark Deeds.

   C. Dad pointed out the garden and yard to Mark Deeds.

4. Why were the green peppers wilted?

   A. The green peppers were wilted because it had been hot.

   B. The green peppers were wilted because it had been cool.

   C. The green peppers were wilted because it was winter.

Directions: Read the story and answer the questions.

5. What advice did Jethro's dad give Mark Deeds?

   A. "We had better jump in the pool."

   B. "We had better go to the garden."

   C. "We had better step back a bit."

6. Who else was in the pool?

   A. Jethro's mom was in the pool.

   B. Jethro's dad was in the pool.

   C. Jethro's sisters were in the pool.

7. What were Jethro's sisters doing?

   A. Jethro's sisters were sunbathing.

   B. Jethro's sisters were floating on pool rafts.

   C. Jethro's sisters were weeding the garden.

8. Which garden bed did Jethro hit?

   A. Jethro hit the bed with the corn.

   B. Jethro hit the bed with the green peppers.

   C. Jethro hit the bed with the lettuce.

9. What is the setting of "The Splash Artist?"

   A. The setting is Jethro's backyard.

   B. The setting is the inside of Jethro's house.

   C. The setting is Jethro's bedroom.

Grammar

cat _____   boy _____

teacher _____   street _____

state _____   classmate _____

Write "noun" or "verb" on the blank:

desks _____   eats _____

hotel _____   chair _____

pinches _____   knocked _____

1.	gift	caught	coat	park
2.	branch	street	runs	Jane
3.	smelled	kids	wrist	road
4.	goat	south	lifted	beach
5.	sailboat	coat	folded	lamps

1. Beth cleaned three _____ at the park.

    benchez   benches   benchs

2. Mom said, "Did you like the two red _____ I got?"

    dresss   dress   dresses

3. We packed our games in lots of _____.

    box   boxes   boxs

4. "Did you clean all the _____ after eating?" asked Tim.

    dishes   dishs   dish

5. We had lots of _____ at home.

    giftes   gift   gifts

boxes   _____   day   _____

bench   _____   cows   _____

raincoat   _____   cats   _____

Mark the Vowel Spelling

If a square has a word with the letter 'a' sounded /a/, make it red. If a square has a word with the letter 'a' sounded /ae/, make it green.

hayride	after	happen	cape	mermaid
yesterday	later	stamp	basic	subway
payment	acorn	parents	major	fragment
places	pad	snail	mattress	math
caper	rainstorm	packing	making	painted

Sound Quest

1. Last May my dad took me on a trip to Spain.

2. We went on a big airplane.

3. We rode on trains.

4. We saw a jail with chains nailed on the sides.

5. We saw lots of paintings and stained glass.

6. We saw the home of a saint.

7. We went on a hike and got caught in the rain.

8. The cupcakes that we had for a snack were awesome!

Directions: Have students circle all of the spellings for the /ae/ sound.

PP2

170 *Unit 3*
© 2013 Core Knowledge Foundation

Scramble Sentence Match

1. her   getting   painted.   Kay   is   face

_____

2. danger!   in   mouse   grave   The   is

_____

3. playing   train.   his   with   is   James

_____

Directions: Have students unscramble the words to make a sentence matching the picture.

Illustrate the Words

Directions: Have students illustrate any /ae/ word from the Spelling Tree. Write the word on the line below the picture.

Mark the Vowel Spellings

If a square has a word with letter 'o' sounded /o/, make it red. If a square has a word with the letter 'o' sounded /oe/, make it green.

hotel	pole	open	shop	soak
oboe	comment	moment	drop	omit
bonus	poster	problem	lot	program
opal	chop	hippo	socks	polo
block	clock	oak	halo	oath

Sound Quest /oe/

Jo, the Inuit, has a home not so far from the North Pole. While her dad hunts, her home is an igloo. It is made from solid ice blocks. You may not think it, but her home is snug inside. Jo's dad keeps a fire going inside the ice home. There is a hole in the roof to let the smoke from the fire escape.

It is freezing at the North Pole. There are lots of frozen slabs of ice. The wind tosses things around as it swoops down from the Pole. If you go to visit Jo, take lots of thick clothing. Take an overcoat and a scarf. Take boots, too. If you don't, you could end up with frozen toes.

'o_e'	'o'	'oa'	'oe'

Directions: Have students read the story and circle all the spellings for /oe/. Then have them sort the circled words in the chart at the bottom of the page.

Crossword Puzzle

Use the clues to fill in the crossword.

coat	broke	home	over	open
coach	hole	moaned	smoke	soap

Side-to-side

2.   When winter is _____, it is spring.

3.   There is _____ from the fire.

7.   I need some _____ to clean my hands.

8.   Is the gate _____?

9.   There is a _____ in my pocket.

Down

1.   I _____ mom's vase when I dropped it.

4.   I _____ because my leg hurt.

5.   The soccer _____ is Mr. Dave.

6.   I would like to go _____ after class.

Yes or No?

Write "yes" or "no."

1. Can a pig ride a bike? _____

2. Do fish stay in a beehive? _____

3. Is green slime good on a sandwich? _____

4. Can you hit a tent stake into the soil? _____

5. Will a pine tree have pine cones? _____

6. Do you like to win a prize when you play a game?
   _____

7. Can a snake smile? _____

8. Can a dog tell time? _____

9. Would a tiger tie a string to a kite? _____

10. Can you read a book inside your classroom?
    _____

Sound Quest /ie/

Last Friday, Mike and his dad visited the zoo in Ohio. Mike was excited at the idea of seeing the tigers, but as soon as he saw them, he became scared. (Mike is only five.) His dad tried to tell Mike that it would be fine, but Mike started weeping. He was scared of the tigers! At last, Mike's dad asked Mike if he'd like to see the hippos instead. Mike nodded and his sobs went away. He was quiet as he and his dad tried to find the hippos. Once they found them, Mike started smiling and chatting with his dad.

Directions: Have students read the story and circle all the spellings for /ie/. Then have them sort the circled words on the chart at the bottom of the page.

'i_e'	'i'	'ie'

Sound Quest /ue/

Directions: Have students read the story and circle all the spellings for /ue/. Then have them sort the circled words on the chart at the bottom of the page.

Last week, my sister and I argued about whether or not unicorns exist. I tried to tell my sister that unicorns are not real, but she did not listen to me. She said that they are just as real as humans. She said that she's seen one. If you ask me, I think she has confused a horse or a mule with a unicorn. We continued our dispute, but then I realized that arguing with her is useless. I will never be able to get her to understand that unicorns don't exist. Besides, it's sort of cute that she thinks unicorns are real.

'u_e'	'u'	'ue'

© 2013 Core Knowledge Foundation

Fill in the Blank

paw	taught	awful	lawn	caught
daughter	hawk	faucet	saw	yawn

1. Miss Smith _____ us to add and subtract numbers.

2. I baited the hook, cast the rod, and _____ a fish.

3. Karen is her parents' _____.

4. That was an _____ storm.

5. Can you cut the grass on the _____?

6. The sink _____ in the kitchen is dripping.

7. I saw you _____, and then I yawned, too.

8. Did you see the _____ chase the mouse?

9. The dog cut his _____.

10. Dad used a _____ to cut the wood.

Directions: Have students complete the sentence with one of the words from the box.

Crossword Puzzle

paw	taught	dawn
lawn	caught	yawn

Side-to-side

2. Grass

4. She _____ me to ride a bike.

6. You do this with your mouth when you are tired.

Down

1. I _____ a fish.

3. This is when the sun rises.

5. An animal's foot

Fill in the Blank

taught	caught	daughter	applaud
sauce	argument	auto	bacon

1. My sister and my mom had an _____ over her messed-up room.

2. My sister is my mom's _____.

3. I like to eat _____ and eggs.

4. We picked tomatoes and made _____.

5. My dad _____ me how to tie my laces.

6. We will _____ when the singers finish.

7. I got _____ taking cake from the cake plate.

8. Another word for a car is an _____.

Yes or No?

Write "yes" or "no."

1. Can a fire make ice cubes? _____

2. Can rain spill from the clouds? _____

3. Is a coat for your legs? _____

4. Is a lamp a parent? _____

5. Is red a number? _____

6. Is ten less than five? _____

7. Can a stump think? _____

8. Do boats float? _____

9. Do cats have six paws? _____

10. Can a fish sing? _____

11. Are boys green? _____

12. Can a mouse add and subtract? _____

13. Can an airplane go fast? _____

14. Are you in fifth grade? _____

Match the Picture

owl	railroad	clothing
volcano	playground	daughter

daughter _____ _____

_____ _____ _____

toad	tornado	hoe
airplane	bathrobe	mailman

_____ _____ _____

_____ _____ _____

Circle the Spellings

Mark the spellings that make up the names of the things that you see. Write the names on the lines.

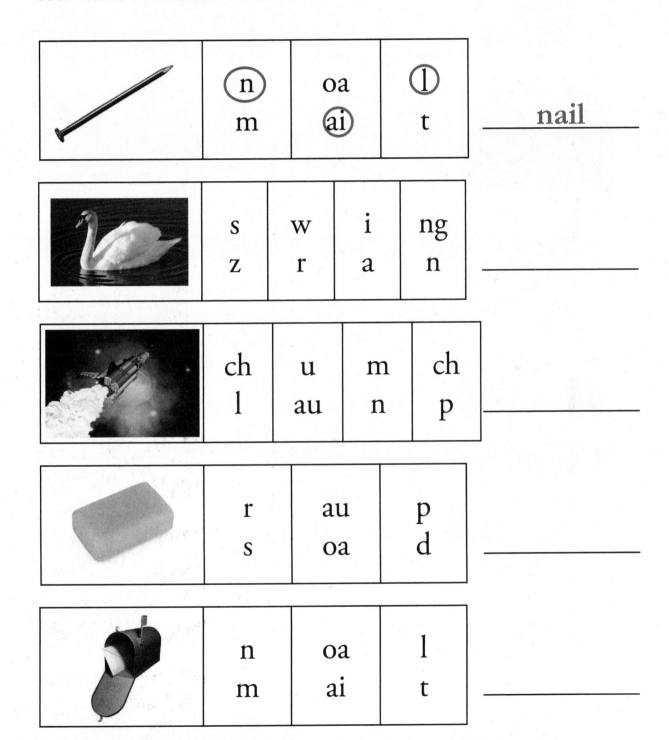

(nail image)	(n) / m	oa / (ai)	(l) / t	nail
(swan image)	s / z	w / r	i / a	ng / n	_____
(rocket image)	ch / l	u / au	m / n	ch / p	_____
(eraser image)	r / s	au / oa	p / d	_____
(mailbox image)	n / m	oa / ai	l / t	_____

	b p	l r	ai au	ng n	_____
	j ch	ai oa	l m		_____
	g b	ai oa	t d		_____
	p c	l oa	l ay		_____
	ch sh	au ai	m n		_____

Match the Words

saucer

hoe

brain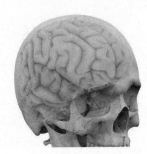

goat

Name _____

Spelling Follow-Up
Lessons 1–5

Write a word from the box on the line in the sentence.

sister	letter	expert	born	sports
short	mark	started	backyard	

1. I like to play in my _____.

2. My _____, Sue, is in fifth grade.

3. Do you like to look at _____ on TV?

4. I got a _____ in the mail!

5. I can't wait to get _____ on my book.

6. Are you an _____ on cars?

7. On your _____; get set; go!

8. I was _____ on August 3.

9. He is too _____ to reach the book on the top shelf.

Spelling Follow-Up
Lessons 6–10

Write a word from the box on the line in the sentence.

page	germs	digits	gray	space
chance	center	carpet		

1. What _____ in the book is the start of "The Spelling Bee"?

2. My cat is _____ and white.

3. We spilled grape drink on the white _____.

4. Use soap to kill _____.

5. Miss Smith will teach us to add with two _____.

6. The sun is in outer _____ .

7. Is there a _____ that you could help me?

8. The _____ of the ham is not cooked.

Spelling Follow-Up
Lessons 11–15

Write a word from the box on the line in each sentence.

knotted	knitting	knocked	whipped
whined	quitting	quacked	wringing

1. The duck _____ as he went to the lake.

2. My sneaker laces are so _____ that even Mom can't fix them!

3. He _____ on the closed gate.

4. Mom used the mixer as she _____ the icing for the cake.

5. My mom is _____ a scarf for me.

6. I am not _____ the team just because I made a mistake.

7. My sister _____ all the way home because she did not get a toy.

8. We are _____ out the wet clothes.

Spelling Follow-Up
Lessons 16–20

Write a word from the box on the line in each sentence.

under	road	open	brave
minus	last	toe	robber

1. Three _____ one is two.

2. The _____ was closed due to the wreck.

3. The stream runs _____ the bridge.

4. The _____ took all of the cash.

5. At _____, we can start.

6. I have a _____ dog named Princess.

7. Is the shop _____ yet?

8. I bumped my foot and stubbed my _____ .

Circle the Nouns

1. The waiter set down the plates.

2. The coat is draped over the chair.

3. The cat is sitting in the road.

4. A letter is in the mailbox.

5. The cup is on the saucer.

6. The team ran three miles.

7. Eggs and milk can be used to make pancakes.

8. The acorn fell from the tree and hit the car.

Directions: Have students circle the nouns in the sentences.

Change Common Nouns to Proper Nouns

Directions: Have students rewrite the sentences, changing the underlined words to proper nouns.

1. Let's go to <u>the store</u>.
    Let's go to Sam's Shop. _____

    _____

2. <u>The boy</u> went to <u>the zoo</u>.

    _____

    _____

3. Kim would like to see <u>a program</u> on TV.

    _____

    _____

4. <u>The man</u> got <u>a book</u>.

    _____

    _____

Change Common Nouns to Proper Nouns

1. <u>The kid</u> went to bed.
    Jim went to bed. _____
    _____

2. <u>The man</u> will drive to <u>a state</u>.
    _____
    _____

3. Let's have a picnic at <u>a park</u>.
    _____
    _____

4. <u>The boys</u> are going to <u>a shop</u>.
    _____
    _____

Directions: Have students rewrite the sentences, changing the underlined words to proper nouns.

Find And Fix

David

~~david~~ and moe are going to red oak park on sunday

with their dog, buster. The park is on jones street. At the

park, they will have a picnic with mister sparks. They will

have hot dogs and root beer. After that, the kids will toss a

stick for buster to fetch. Then david and moe will hop on

their bikes and ride back to their home on raven street.

Sort the Nouns

Common Noun	Proper Noun

Directions: Have students write the common and proper nouns from the previous page on this chart.

Identify Common and Proper Nouns

Directions: Have students circle the common nouns and draw a box around the proper nouns in each sentence.

1. [Jeff] is reading a (book.)

2. I want to get a book named *Where the Red Fern Grows*.

3. Alex likes that cartoon.

4. The class is going to see *Batman*.

5. Kate is having dinner at a diner.

6. The men are having subs at Stan's Snack Shop.

7. My best bud is June Lee.

8. Mom, can Max and Bob visit the Bronx Zoo with us?

9. Dad slipped and fell on his knees.

10. Fern made a robot in the basement.

Make the Plurals

1. road ___**roads**___

2. braid _____

3. folder _____

4. couch _____

5. dish _____

6. six _____

7. cake _____

8. hawk _____

9. magnet _____

10. soap _____

Directions: Have students write the plural form of each word.

Make the Plurals

1. The <u>fox</u> sat on the ground.
    The foxes sat on the ground. _____

2. Their <u>boss</u> went to the store.

    _____

    _____

3. When did they get the <u>dress</u>?

    _____

    _____

4. The men are in the <u>trench</u>.

    _____

    _____

5. We broke the <u>dish</u>.

    _____

    _____

6. Mop up your <u>mess</u>.

    _____

    _____

Directions: Have students rewrite each sentence to make the underlined word plural.

Make the Plurals

1. lake ___lakes___

2. tray _____

3. bus _____

4. torch _____

5. dish _____

6. box _____

7. match _____

8. plate _____

9. teapot _____

10. wish _____

Directions: Have students write the plural form of each word.

Synonyms

chant	awesome	flames	costume	fresh
like	dirt	leap	street	nut

Directions: Have students write the synonym from the box on the line beside the word.

1. grand _____

2. outfit _____

3. enjoy _____

4. sing _____

5. acorn _____

6. a fire _____

7. jump _____

8. road _____

9. clean _____

10. soil _____

Name _____

Synonyms

auto	carpet	huge	stretch	bandit
torn	blend	silent	hero	minus

1. car _____
2. subtract _____
3. big _____
4. reach _____
5. rug _____
6. outlaw _____
7. ripped _____
8. mix _____
9. a brave man _____
10. quiet _____

Directions: Have students write the synonym from the box on the line beside the word.

PP34

Unit 3 **233**

© 2013 Core Knowledge Foundation

Antonyms

cool	broken	over	stop	close
near	shrink	short	white	glad

1. under _____

2. far _____

3. sad _____

4. tall _____

5. fixed _____

6. stretch _____

7. black _____

8. go _____

9. open _____

10. hot _____

Directions: Have students write the antonym from the box on the line beside the correct word.

Antonyms

attic	under	thin	start
add	after	her	moon

1. before _____

2. basement _____

3. subtract _____

4. end _____

5. his _____

6. thick _____

7. over _____

8. sun _____

Action Verbs

1. I run to the playground.

2. Rabbits hop in their pens.

3. Frogs croak at dark.

4. The sun shines all day.

5. Snakes slither over rocks.

6. The wind sweeps over the plains.

7. I ate cake.

8. Trees bend under the ice.

9. We sing in the morning.

10. Farmer Jim milks the cows.

Directions: Have students draw a wavy line under the action verb in each sentence.

Name _____

Nouns and Verbs

Circle the nouns. Underline the verbs.

sister	begged	hay
sees	pitching	mom
smelled	dog	eat
skipping	house	running
mouse	shiver	groan
taught	teacher	zipper
zipping	shining	sneaker
geese	boy	chimp
tasted	dad	bed

Grammar

Directions: Have students make plural nouns out of the singular nouns. Write the sentences correctly using correct capitalization, end marks, and quotation marks, if needed.

cat	**cats**	bench	**benches**
fox	_____	chain	_____
class	_____	hand	_____
dish	_____	boat	_____

1. which park will you visit on sunday

   _____

   _____

2. i like camping in the tent at lake lee, said tim

   _____

   _____

3. can sam and i go with her to see miss harper? asked jack

   _____

   _____

4. the trip to the farm was awesome for the class

   _____

   _____

Adding –ed and –ing

Add –ed or –ing to each word and write it in the blank.

1. Spiders are good at _____ insects in their webs.
    (catch)

2. Insects stick to a spider's web. But when the spider is
    _____ the web, it does not stick to it.
    (spin)

3. Spiders use their spinnerets when _____ a new web.
    (spin)

4. When the insects escaped, they _____ the web.
    (destroy)

5. The spider _____ a meal because the insects got
    (miss)
    away.

6. The spider didn't wait and will have the web _____ in
    (fix)
    no time.

7. As soon as the web is _____, the spider waits to catch
    (fix)
    more bugs.

8. Spiders are good helpers for gardeners. They spend their days
    _____ pests.
    (catch)

Interview

1. The name of my person is

    _____

    _____

2. I chose this person because

    _____

    _____

    _____

3. What is interesting about my person is

    _____

    _____

    _____

4. One more thing I think is interesting is

    _____

    _____

    _____

Directions: Have students pretend they are the writer of a magazine similar to Kids Excel. Tell them to pretend to interview a person and to use this sheet to help plan their story.

/ue/

_____

_____

_____

_____

_____

_____

_____

_____

_____

_____

_____

_____

_____

_____

_____

Directions: Have students write a story using at least 5 words from the /ue/ Spelling Tree.

/oe/

Directions: Have students write a story using at least 5 words from the /oe/ Spelling Tree.

/ae/

Directions: Have students write a story using at least 5 words from the /ae/ Spelling Tree.

Letting the Ducks Out

1. What do they call rock skipping in the United Kingdom?

   _____

   _____

2. What do they call it in Spain?

   _____

   _____

3. What is the biggest number of skips ever seen?

   _____

   _____

4. How did Moe do when he skipped rocks in the United Kingdom?

   _____

   _____

5. What is Moe's goal for the next trip?

   _____

   _____

6. Do you have goals? What are they?

   _____

   _____

Directions: Have students answer the questions using complete sentences.

How to Skip a Rock

1. Moe Keller excels at _____ .

    A. spelling

    B. skipping rocks

    C. swimming

2. What is a good skipping rock?

    A. A good skipping rock is jagged.

    B. A good skipping rock is huge and sharp.

    C. A good skipping rock is smooth and flat.

3. If you want to skip a rock, why do you have to snap your wrist when you let the rock go?

    A. You have to snap your wrist to get the rock to spin.

    B. You have to snap your wrist to make the rock hot.

    C. You have to snap your wrist to get the rock to stop spinning.

4. What is a plonk?

    A. A plonk is a rock that skips ten times.

    B. A plonk is a rock that sinks without skipping.

    C. A plonk is a kid who skips rocks.

Directions: Have students reread the story and answer the questions.

5. Have you ever skipped a rock? Are you good at it? Write a story using the "W" questions.

Who?_____

_____

What?_____

_____

_____

When?_____

_____

_____

Where?_____

_____

_____

Why?_____

_____

The Math Contest

Directions: Have students reread the story and answer the questions using complete sentences.

1. Did Mark Deeds solve Problem 1?

    _____

    _____

    _____

2. How long did it take him?

    _____

    _____

    _____

3. What happened when Mark Deeds looked at Problem 2?

    _____

    _____

    _____

4. Who is Dr. Chang?

_____

_____

_____

_____

5. What did Dr. Chang do to make Mark Deeds feel better?

_____

_____

_____

_____

6. Do you like math? Why or why not?

_____

_____

_____

_____

The Winner

1. Who ended up winning the math contest?

_____

_____

_____

_____

2. Where is Hans from?

_____

_____

_____

_____

3. How well did Hans do on the math test?

_____

_____

_____

_____

Directions: Have students reread the story and answer the questions using complete sentences.

4. How did Hans excel at math?

_____

_____

_____

_____

5. Can you explain why Hans likes math so much?

_____

_____

_____

_____

Too Much Mail

Directions: Have students reread the story and answer the questions using complete sentences.

1. Why was Hans in the paper?

   _____

   _____

   _____

2. Who is sending Hans mail?

   _____

   _____

   _____

3. Why are they sending Hans mail?

   _____

   _____

   _____

4. List some colleges that sent Hans mail.

_____

_____

_____

_____

5. Why is getting too much mail a good problem to have?

_____

_____

_____

_____

6. Do you want to go to college one day? Why or why not?

_____

_____

_____

_____

The Art of the Splash

1. How long did it take Jethro to get good at splashing?

    A. It took him five jumps.

    B. It took him five weeks.

    C. It took him five summers.

2. Which contest did Jethro win?

    A. He won a spelling bee.

    B. He won a math contest.

    C. He won a splash contest.

3. What was his prize?

    A. His prize was one hundred bucks.

    B. His prize was ten bucks.

    C. His prize was five hundred bucks.

4. Match the kids with the skill at which they excel. (Feel free to look back at the book if you need to.)

Hans Brucker   swimming

Jethro Otter   math

Kim Castro   splashing

Kit Winter   jumping rope

Moe Keller   spelling

Gail Day   skipping rocks

5. What is a skill at which you excel?

_____

_____

_____

_____

_____

_____

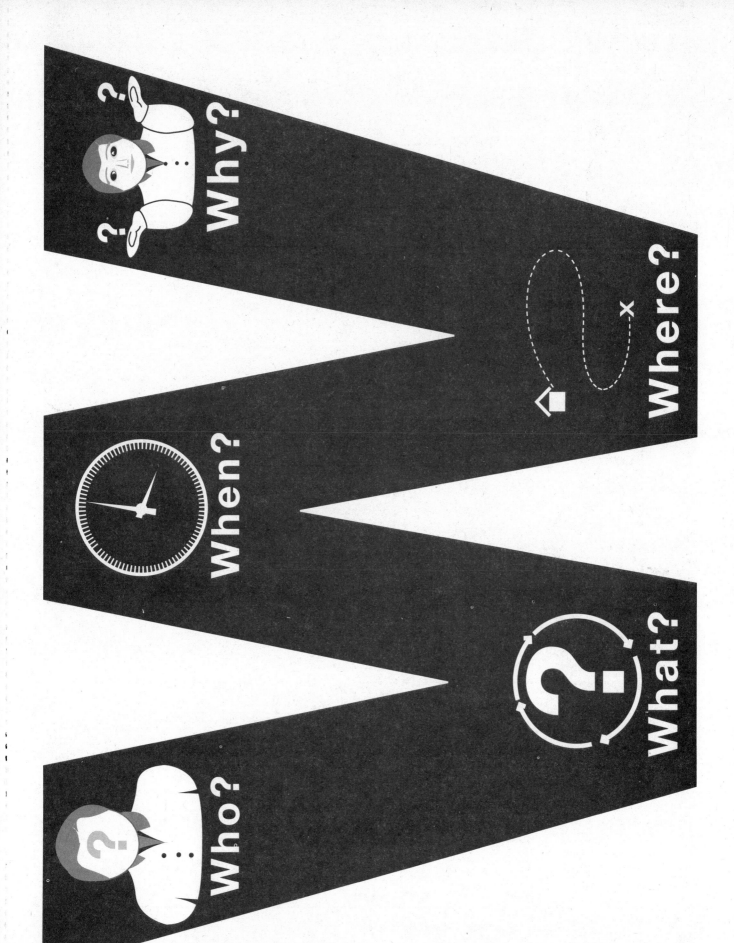

CORE KNOWLEDGE LANGUAGE ARTS

SERIES EDITOR-IN-CHIEF
E. D. Hirsch, Jr.

PRESIDENT
Linda Bevilacqua

EDITORIAL STAFF
Carolyn Gosse, Senior Editor - Preschool
Khara Turnbull, Materials Development Manager
Michelle L. Warner, Senior Editor - Listening & Learning

Mick Anderson
Robin Blackshire
Maggie Buchanan
Paula Coyner
Sue Fulton
Sara Hunt
Erin Kist
Robin Luecke
Rosie McCormick
Cynthia Peng
Liz Pettit
Ellen Sadler
Deborah Samley
Diane Auger Smith
Sarah Zelinke

DESIGN AND GRAPHICS STAFF
Scott Ritchie, Creative Director

Kim Berrall
Michael Donegan
Liza Greene
Matt Leech
Bridget Moriarty
Lauren Pack

CONSULTING PROJECT MANAGEMENT SERVICES
ScribeConcepts.com

ADDITIONAL CONSULTING SERVICES
Ang Blanchette
Dorrit Green
Carolyn Pinkerton

ACKNOWLEDGMENTS

These materials are the result of the work, advice, and encouragement of numerous individuals over many years. Some of those singled out here already know the depth of our gratitude; others may be surprised to find themselves thanked publicly for help they gave quietly and generously for the sake of the enterprise alone. To helpers named and unnamed we are deeply grateful.

CONTRIBUTORS TO EARLIER VERSIONS OF THESE MATERIALS
Susan B. Albaugh, Kazuko Ashizawa, Nancy Braier, Kathryn M. Cummings, Michelle De Groot, Diana Espinal, Mary E. Forbes, Michael L. Ford, Ted Hirsch, Danielle Knecht, James K. Lee, Diane Henry Leipzig, Martha G. Mack, Liana Mahoney, Isabel McLean, Steve Morrison, Juliane K. Munson, Elizabeth B. Rasmussen, Laura Tortorelli, Rachael L. Shaw, Sivan B. Sherman, Miriam E. Vidaver, Catherine S. Whittington, Jeannette A. Williams

We would like to extend special recognition to Program Directors Matthew Davis and Souzanne Wright who were instrumental to the early development of this program.

SCHOOLS
We are truly grateful to the teachers, students, and administrators of the following schools for their willingness to field test these materials and for their invaluable advice: Capitol View Elementary, Challenge Foundation Academy (IN), Community Academy Public Charter School, Lake Lure Classical Academy, Lepanto Elementary School, New Holland Core Knowledge Academy, Paramount School of Excellence, Pioneer Challenge Foundation Academy, New York City PS 26R (The Carteret School), PS 30X (Wilton School), PS 50X (Clara Barton School), PS 96Q, PS 102X (Joseph O. Loretan), PS 104Q (The Bays Water), PS 214K (Michael Friedsam), PS 223Q (Lyndon B. Johnson School), PS 308K (Clara Cardwell), PS 333Q (Goldie Maple Academy), Sequoyah Elementary School, South Shore Charter Public School, Spartanburg Charter School, Steed Elementary School, Thomas Jefferson Classical Academy, Three Oaks Elementary, West Manor Elementary.

And a special thanks to the CKLA Pilot Coordinators Anita Henderson, Yasmin Lugo-Hernandez, and Susan Smith, whose suggestions and day-to-day support to teachers using these materials in their classrooms was critical.